EGMONT
We bring stories to life

First published in Great Britain in 2016 by Egmont UK Limited,
The Yellow Building, I Nicholas Road, London WII 4AN

Written by Mara Alperin
Designed by Jeannette O'Toole

© 2016 Disney Enterprises, Inc.

ISBN 978 I 4052 8342 7
63791/I
Printed in Italy

This **Moana** Annual belongs to:

Lyla Violet Booth

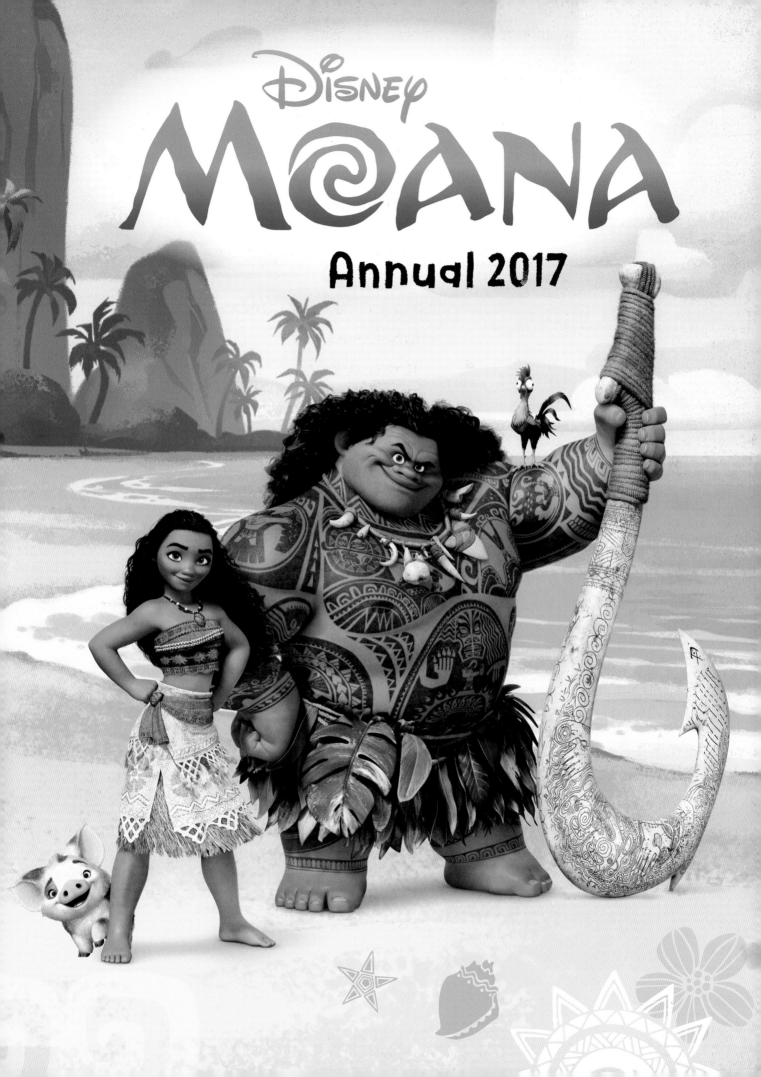

What's Inside

The Heart of Te Fiti

Many thousands of years ago, the mother island Te Fiti emerged from the ocean. Te Fiti's heart had the power to create life itself!

And so new islands sprang up, and the people and animals all flourished. Every year, the people would wayfind through the ocean to find new islands.

But the heart of Te Fiti was stolen! Darkness fell, and powerful monsters like Te Kā, the lava monster, awoke. The people stopped sailing, and slowly the islands began to die.

The heart of Te Fiti was lost at sea for hundreds of years. Then one day it washed up on the island of Motunui. It would stay there, kept safe in a special necklace, until the day when someone would journey beyond the reef and across the great ocean to restore the heart of Te Fiti ...

Meet Moana

Everything you need to know about Moana ...

Moana is **brave** and **adventurous**. She's always **dreamed** about going out onto the **ocean!**

Her **father** is the **Chief** of Motunui.

She **cares** about her **people** and wants to do what's **right!**

When Moana feels strongly about something, she **never** gives up!

Are you a WAYFINDER?

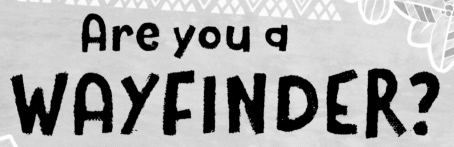

Moana is a born wayfinder. Are you a wayfinder too? Tick all the special talents you have that will help with wayfinding:

 I like adventure

 I like to travel

 I like to swim

 I like to be outside

 I can find my way around without getting lost

 I like to help others

 I am a friend to animals

WELL DONE!

Family and Friends

Everything you need to know about Moana's family and friends!

Chief Tui

He is Moana's father and the leader of Motunui.

Chief Tui is happy staying on the island where it's safe, and he wants Moana to be happy too.

Like Moana, he can be very stubborn!

Gramma Tala

She is a wonderful storyteller, especially when it comes to telling the legend of Te Fiti.

She loves splashing and dancing with the waves.

Gramma Tala may be a bit eccentric ... but she loves Moana very much!

I'm the chief!

Listen to the ocean!

Heihei

Heihei is the village rooster. He walks around and tries to eat everything.

He can be a bit clumsy.

Sometimes the villagers find Heihei a bit annoying, but Moana makes sure that nobody eats him!

Pua

Pua is Moana's pet pig. He has been at her side ever since she was a little girl.

He has the energy of a puppy, and never stops moving.

Pua is very loyal – he'll do anything for Moana!

Bagock!

Moana is my best friend!

Which Pua is the odd one out?

a   b   c   d

Answers on page 67.

Feathered Friends

Clumsy Heihei has gotten himself and Pua in a muddle! Number the pieces from 1 to 6 to put the picture in the correct order.

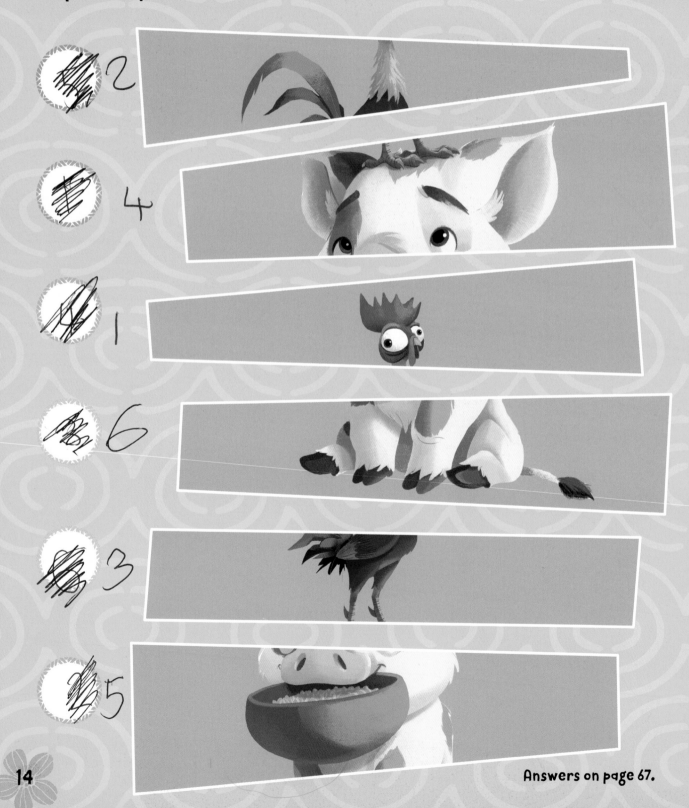

2

4

1

6

3

5

14

Answers on page 67.

Where's the Water?

Moana has been an animal lover ever since she was a little girl. Help her guide this baby turtle back to the water so he can swim home.

START

FINISH

Answers on page 67.

The Ocean Chooses Moana

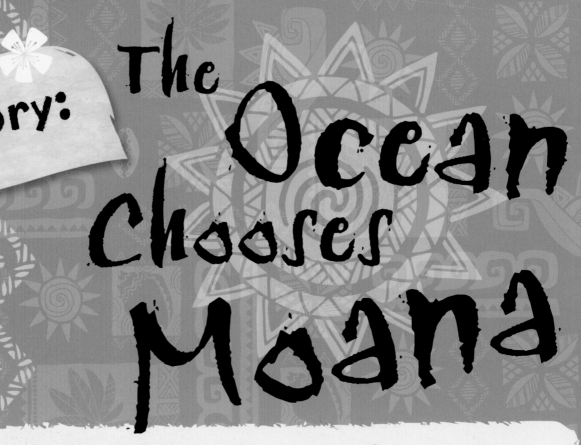

For as long as she could remember, Moana was drawn to the ocean. She felt like it was calling to her, and she dreamed about going out on a voyage, like her ancestors did many, many years ago.

But Moana's father – Chief Tui – forbid anyone from going beyond the reef. Chief Tui loved his people, and he wanted them to stay on the island of Motunui where it was safe. Most of all, he wanted Moana to be happy on Motunui, so she could be the next great chief of their people.

As the years passed, the fish around the island started to disappear and the crops began to die.

One day, a fisherman warned that there was almost no food left. The people of Motunui would soon go hungry, so Moana suggested going beyond the reef to look for food. This did not make Chief Tui happy!

Gramma Tala knew that Moana was right. Late at night, she lead Moana to a hidden cavern – the cavern of the wayfinders. Gramma Tala explained that to save the island from darkness, Moana must journey beyond the reef, find the demigod Maui, and bring him across the great ocean to restore the heart of Te Fiti.

Gramma Tala gave Moana her special necklace with the heart of Te Fiti inside. The ocean had given it to Moana when she was very little, and Gramma Tala had kept it safe for her. "The ocean chose you, Moana," Gramma Tala whispered. "Look to the stars. You will find a way."

Hidden message

Use the code to work out Gramma Tala's message for Moana.

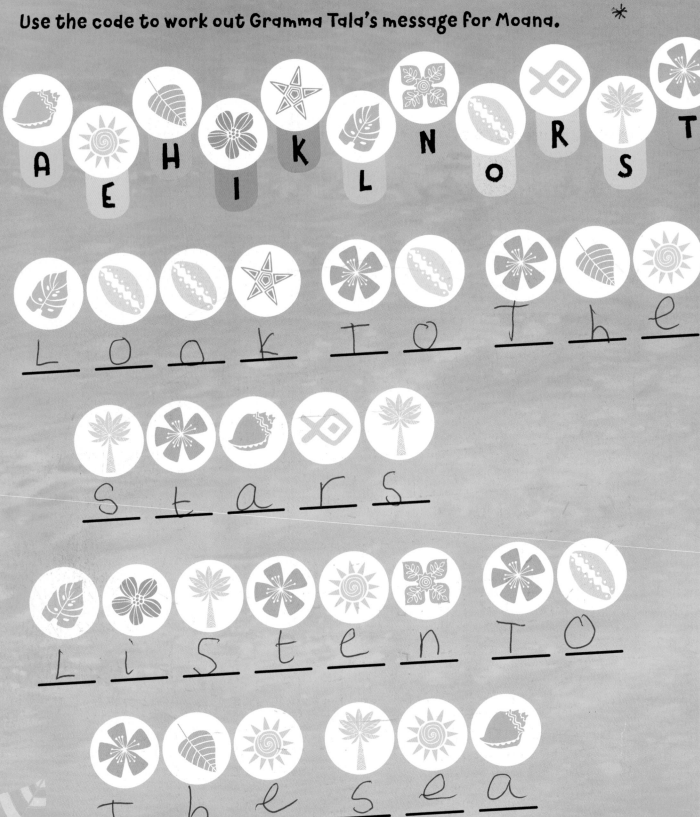

A E H I K L N O R S T

L O O K <u>T</u>O <u>T</u>h<u>e</u>

S t a r s

L i s t e n T O

T i h e s e a

Answers on page 67.

Wayfinder Wordsearch

A wayfinder is an expert voyager who travels across the ocean. Can you find all 10 words in the wordsearch? Words read forwards, up, down, diagonally and backwards, too.

S	P	L	E	R	W	A	V	E	S	Y	Q
E	T	D	S	Q	A	O	Z	C	G	K	I
D	W	U	V	O	Y	A	G	E	R	S	O
I	A	S	X	H	F	X	E	A	D	N	B
T	D	T	U	A	I	H	V	N	X	R	A
Y	M	O	T	U	N	U	I	P	M	L	D
O	B	C	A	P	D	W	G	C	O	N	Z
E	T	E	S	X	E	L	Y	O	A	K	B
W	S	A	C	O	R	A	L	S	N	P	A
O	H	N	E	D	Z	O	W	K	A	X	J

MOANA ✓

MOTUNUI ✓

VOYAGER ✓

WAYFINDER

OCEAN

WAVES ✓

WINDS

TIDES ✓

CORAL ✓

SAND

Answers on page 67.

Meet Maui

Everything you need to know about Maui!

Maui is a demigod – half mortal, half god.

He is **super-strong**, and thinks he's the best at **everything!**

His magical tattoo of Mini Maui can move!

Maui can be a bit of a **trickster**, but he wants to be a **true hero.**

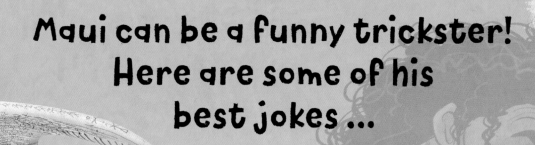

Maui can be a funny trickster! Here are some of his best jokes ...

1

How do you cut the ocean in half?

With a sea-saw!

2

Why don't oysters like to share their toys?

Because they are shellfish!

3

What did the ocean say to the beach?

Nothing – it just waved!

4

What do sharks like to eat for dinner?

Fish and ships!

5

What kind of fish come out at night?

Star fish!

Now read about how Moana and Maui met ...

Maui's Island

After a great storm, Moana found herself shipwrecked on a sandy island. Suddenly, a huge figure appeared – it was Maui, the demigod of the wind and sea. Gramma Tala had told Moana that Maui was once considered the greatest hero in the land, but then the trickster had stolen the heart of Te Fiti, unleashing the darkness.

Maui still thought he was a great hero, and he told Moana about all the heroic things he had done – lassoing the sun, harnessing the winds for sailing and pulling islands from the sea.

Bravely, Moana retorted, "You are NOT a hero! You stole the heart of Te Fiti. And you will board my boat, sail across the sea and put it back!"

Maui didn't want to go with Moana. He tried to steal her boat and sail away without her, but the ocean was on Moana's side. No matter where Maui steered the boat, the ocean swept up Moana and moved her in front of Maui. Soon Maui realised that he didn't have a choice!

As Maui and Moana sailed on together, they saw a raft with creatures that looked like coconuts. They were Kakamora – fierce and dangerous pirates! The Kakamora threw their sharp spears at Moana and Maui, who barely got away!

"We'll never make it all the way, not without my hook," said Maui. He explained that his hook gave him the power to shape-shift into different animals. Maui's hook had been lost, and Maui thought that Tamatoa the scavenger might have it.

So off they set in the direction of Tamatoa's Lair to find Maui's lost hook!

kakamora
Confusion

The kakamora are hiding in the forest. How many kakamora can you spot hiding in the leaves?

24

Answers on page 67.

Wayfinding

Wayfinders use the sun, moon, waves and tides to navigate through the ocean. Put your finger on the START, then follow the path through the matching wave shapes. If you're a talented wayfinder like Moana, you'll make it all the way to the FINISH.

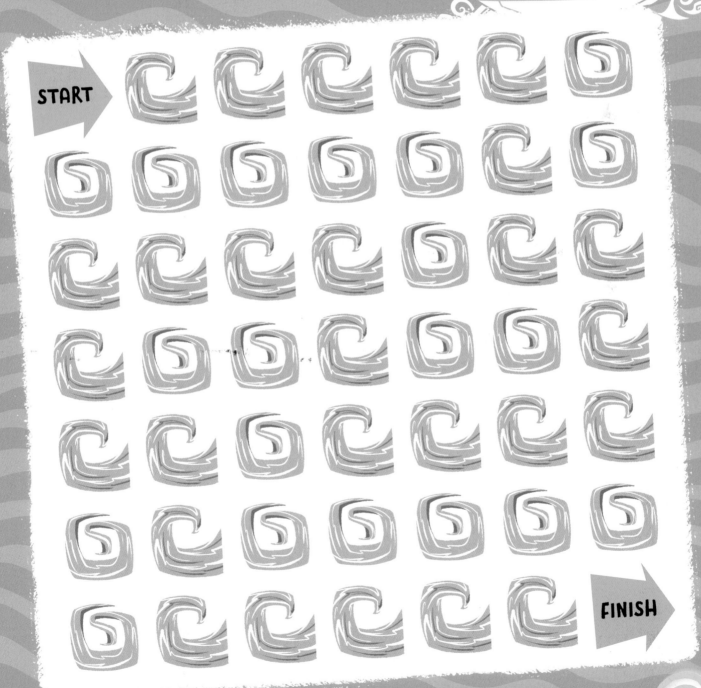

Answers on page 67.

Building a Boat

What you need:
A piece of paper

To go out on ocean adventures, you'll need a boat!
Fold your own in this step-by-step guide.

1

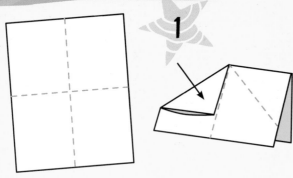

Crease a piece of paper lengthways, then fold it in half. Fold over the corners to meet the crease.

2

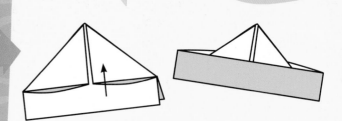

Fold both corners over then fold up the bottom edge on both sides.

3

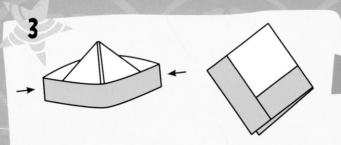

Push the ends in and flatten.

4

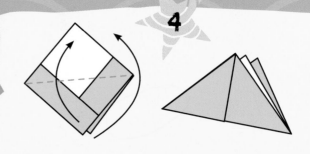

Fold up both sides and flatten.

5

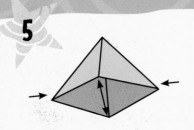

Pull sides apart and flatten.

6

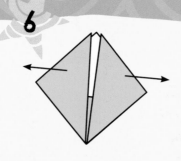

Pull the ends out.

7

Pull the bottom straight and flatten the boat out.

Your boat is ready to sail!

knot Again!

Have you got a piece of string or rope? Good!
Then you can learn to tie sailor knots just like Moana.

Figure 8 knot

1 Cross over the string to make a loop, as shown here.

2 Take the string from the left, and cross over the string on the right.

3 Thread the string through the loop from the back.

4 Pull the top string and the bottom string tight to form the knot.

You've just tied a figure 8 knot!

Spot the Difference

Moana and Maui are off on their adventure.
Can you spot 10 differences between these two pictures?
Colour in a shell each time you find a difference.

1

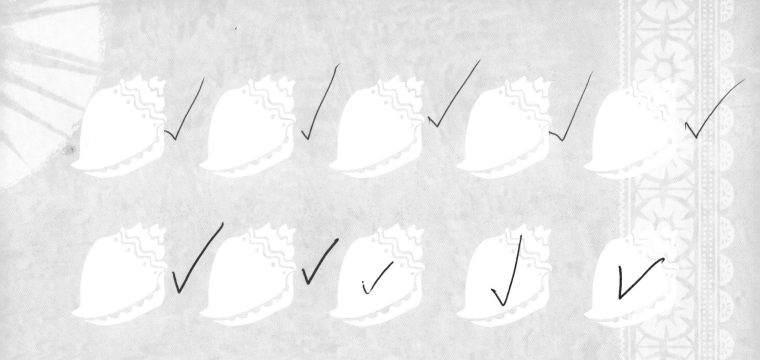

2

Answers on page 67.

Look to the Stars

Gramma Tala told Moana to use the stars to guide her. For thousands of years, people have navigated the seas by using the stars as a map. Here are a few constellations. Can you spot them in the sky at night?

The Big Dipper
This group of stars is shaped like a giant spoon!

Orion
This constellation is named after the great hunter from Greek mythology. The three bright stars make up his belt!

Leo

This group of stars looks like a lion about to pounce!

Cassiopeia

This constellation is named for the beautiful but vain queen sitting in her chair.

Now connect some of these stars below to make your very own constellation!

My **constellation** is called:

....

Tricky Teasers

See if you can solve Maui's tricky puzzles!
Figure out the pattern and then draw in what comes next!

a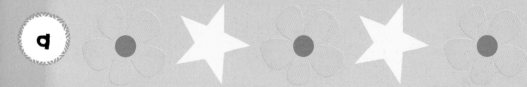

b

c

d

Answers on page 67.

Heihei has wandered off. Can you help lead him back to the boat? Do the sums and follow the correct answers to find the path.

$6 + 2 =$ 8

8   7

$4 - 1 =$ $2 + 3 =$

2   3   4

$3 + 6 =$ $5 - 4 =$ $7 - 2 =$

9   2   1   5

a   b   c   d

Answers on page 67.

Cool Colouring

Colour in these pictures of Heihei, using your brightest colours!

we KNOW

the WAY!

Be **true** to your **heart**

© 2016 Disney

Follow the stars

CUT ALONG HERE

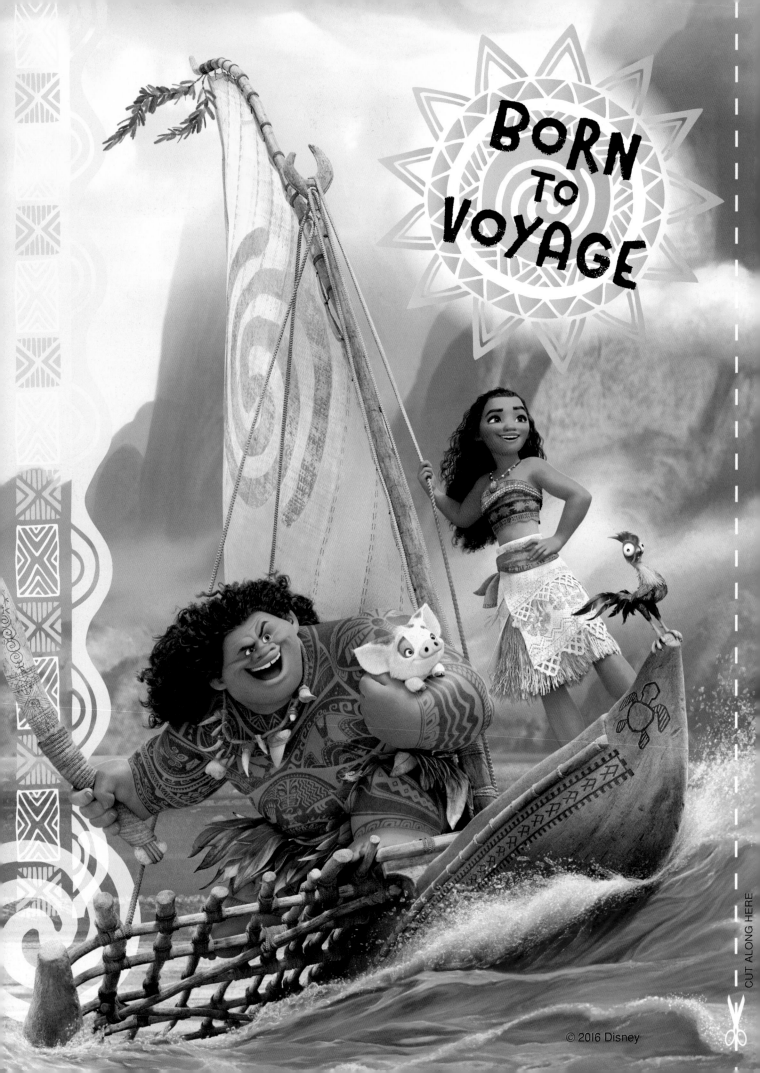

BORN TO VOYAGE

CUT ALONG HERE

Big Picture

Can you spot these close-ups in the big picture?

a

b

c

d

e

f

Answers on page 68.

Make a Necklace

Gramma Tala gave Moana her necklace, and she wears it all the time. Now you can make your own special necklace. You can use a seashell from the ocean, or a small rock.

What you need:
Small seashell or rock
50g flour
60g salt
50ml water
Food colouring (optional)
Pencil or straw
Baking tray
Ribbon

Step 1:
Make the salt dough

In a large bowl, mix together the flour, salt and water. If you have food colouring, you can add it now. Knead the dough until smooth. If the dough feels a bit sticky, you may want to add a bit more flour.

Always ask an adult to help you!

Step 2:
Make the pendant

Roll the dough into a little ball. Press down to flatten, and add your seashell or rock. If you have lots of shells, you can make more than one! Use a pencil or straw to make a hole near the top.

Step 3:
Bake your pendant

Ask an adult to put your pendants on a baking tray and bake them at 120°C/250°F/Gas Mark ½ for 2-3 hours, or until the dough is completely dry. Use a heat-proof cloth to remove the tray from the oven and allow the pendants to cool completely.

Step 4:
Make your necklace

Thread a ribbon through the pendant. Make sure that the ribbon is not too long, but that it is long enough for the loop to go over your head. Now you have a necklace just like Moana's!

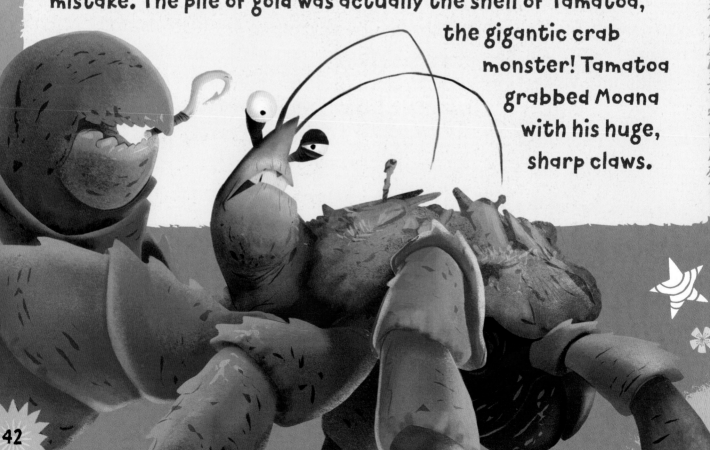

The Lair of Tamatoa

The entrance to Tamatoa's Lair was through Lalotai – the realm of monsters! Maui and Moana had to jump through a swirling vortex ... and then avoid being eaten by the giant monsters!

As Moana dodged a slimy sea monster, she caught a glimpse of a hook in a nearby cave. Moana crept inside the lair. Sitting on top of a glittering pile of gold and treasure was Maui's hook!

But when Moana tried to pick up the hook, she realised her mistake. The pile of gold was actually the shell of Tamatoa, the gigantic crab monster! Tamatoa grabbed Moana with his huge, sharp claws.

"You're a long way from home," Tamatoa crooned. "And you look tasty."

Suddenly, Maui leaped in, grabbing Moana and his hook. "It's Maui time!" he called. Maui tried to shape-shift, but he was out of practice and it didn't work. Tamatoa clicked his giant claws and came closer!

Then Moana had an idea. Tamatoa liked shiny things, so she pretended to throw the heart of Te Fiti deep into the cave. While Tamatoa ran off to find it, Moana and Maui grabbed the hook and escaped!

Moana still had the real heart, and now Maui had his hook. Moana helped Maui practise shape-shifting, until he could turn into a hawk, then a shark, then back again.

"Next stop – Te Fiti!" said Moana.

Shadow Match

Darkness is falling across the island! Can you help match Moana's friends to their shadows?

a

b

c

1

2

3

Answers on page 68.

Tamatoa's Treasure

The great monster Tamatoa loves to hoard shiny treasure. Colour in only the squares with a tick to find the hidden picture!

Answers on page 68.

Odd one Out

Which one of these pictures of Moana is the odd one out?

a

b

c

d

e

f

Answers on page 68.

Memory Challenge

Take a look at this picture, then hide it under a piece of paper.
Now try and answer the quiz questions below.

1 Who is on the boat with Maui?

2 How many sails does the boat have?

3 True or false: Moana is carrying an oar.

4 True or false: There are clouds in the sky.

5 True or false: Maui is wearing a necklace.

Answers on page 68.

perfect Pairs

Look at all the leaves and shells on the beach.
Can you match up the nine pairs and find one left over?

a

b

c

d

e

f

g

h

i

j

k

l

Write the pairs below. The first has been done for you.

a & q ⎪ & ⎪ &

 & ⎪ & ⎪ &

 & ⎪ & ⎪ &

Which item doesn't have a pair?

m

n

P

o

q

s

r

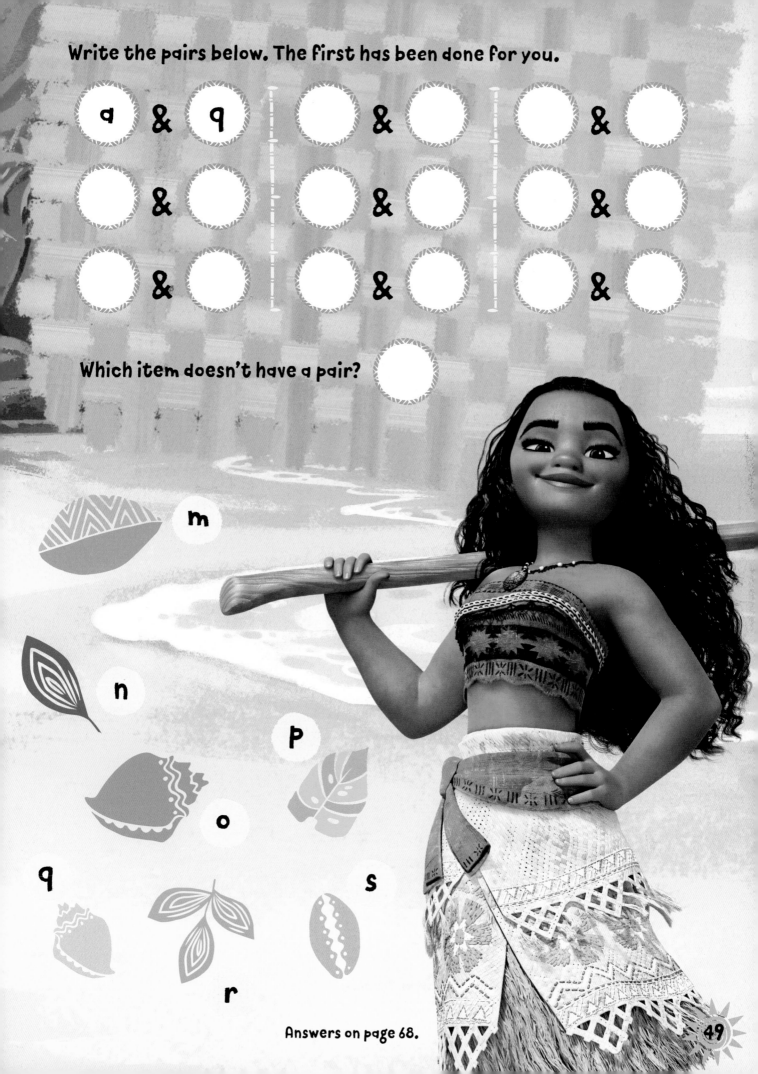

The Heart is Restored

Moana and Maui sailed towards Te Fiti, where a thick cloud of ash was waiting for them. It was Te Kā, the giant lava monster!

Te Kā hurled fireballs of lava at Moana, but Moana skilfully dodged them in her boat. As Moana closed in on Te Fiti, Maui transformed into a hawk and soared off to battle Te Kā. Moana raced up the sandy bank with her necklace from Gramma Tala, returning the heart of Te Fiti!

In a swirl of deep green leaves, Te Fiti rose up and carried Moana and Maui back onto the island. Moana knew that Te Fiti was thankful and had forgiven Maui for having stolen the heart so many years ago.

Moana gave Maui a big hug. Although the trickster had been difficult and unwilling at first, he had proved himself a great hero. Moana knew they would be friends for life.

Back at Motunui, the island was blossoming! Black and dying plants suddenly came back to life, and colourful fish swam through the lagoon.

When Moana returned, the whole village was waiting for her. Moana had saved Motunui and all her people. She was a true wayfinder, and would lead her people on many voyages in the years to come.

Maui Morphing

With his magical hook, Maui can shape-shift into different animals.
Use the space below to draw what you think he will shape shift into next!

shape-shifting Quiz

Which island animal should you shape-shift into? Take this fun quiz to find out!

1 How would your friends describe you?

a ◯ playful   **b** ◯ outgoing   **c** ◯ wise

2 What do you like to do for fun?

a ◯ go to the beach   **b** ◯ go to the park with my friends   **c** ◯ read a good book

3 What's the best way to travel?

a ◯ swimming   **b** ◯ running   **c** ◯ flying

Mostly a's
You are very smart, and like to approach life with humour and joy. Shape-shift into a **dolphin**, and you can go swimming and leap through the waves!

Mostly b's
You are compassionate and not afraid to stand up for your friends. Shape-shift into a **mongoose**, and you can spend the day running and playing with your friends.

Mostly c's
You are responsible and focused, and your friends come to you for advice. Shape-shift into a **hawk**, and you can soar through the skies above!

53

How Well do you know Moana?

1

Where does Moana live?

a. ◯ Maranaki

b. ◯ Motunui

c. ◯ Mininui

2

Moana's pet Pua is what type of animal?

a. ◯ dog   b. ◯ cat

c. ◯ pig

3

What does Gramma Tala give Moana to take on her voyage?

a. ◯ a necklace

b. ◯ a bracelet

c. ◯ a ring

4

What is Maui?

a. ◯ a demigod   b. ◯ a fisherman

c. ◯ a giant crab monster

5

Who has Maui's hook?

a. ◯ The Kakamora   b. ◯ Tamatoa   c. ◯ Te Fiti

6

What does Moana use to navigate the ocean?

a. ◯ a compass

b. ◯ a mobile phone

c. ◯ the stars

7

What is the giant lava monster called?

a. ◯ Te La   b. ◯ Te Kā

c. ◯ Te Pa

8

Who is this?

a. ◯ Pua

b. ◯ Tamatoa

c. ◯ Heihei

Answers on page 68.

55

Navigation Challenge

Can you take this tricky wayfinder challenge? Follow the directions to Moana, picking up her friends on the way.

START

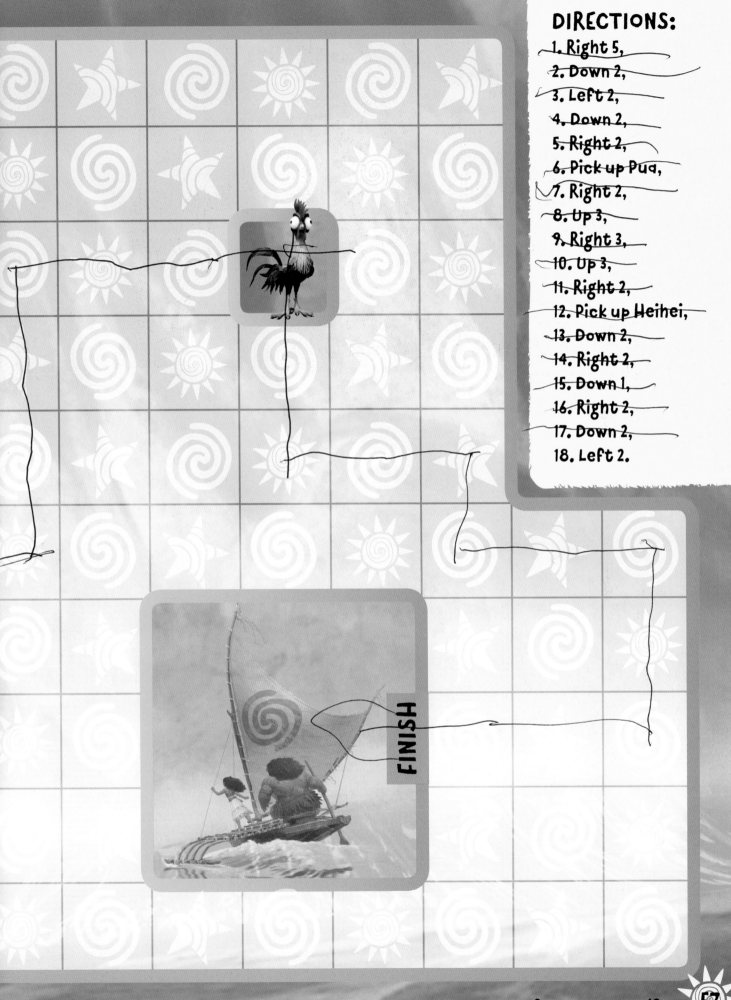

Answers on page 68.

DIRECTIONS:
1. Right 5,
2. Down 2,
3. Left 2,
4. Down 2,
5. Right 2,
6. Pick up Pua,
7. Right 2,
8. Up 3,
9. Right 3,
10. Up 3,
11. Right 2,
12. Pick up Heihei,
13. Down 2,
14. Right 2,
15. Down 1,
16. Right 2,
17. Down 2,
18. Left 2.

FINISH

57

Ocean Emotion

Moana has always felt a deep connection with the ocean. What do you like to do at the beach?

- Go swimming
- Build a sandcastle
- Ride a jet ski
- Go snorkelling
- Eat ice cream
- Collect seashells
- Go rockpooling
- Splash my friends!

A Puzzling Scene

Can you find the missing jigsaw piece to fill each gap in the picture?

a

b

c

d

e

Answers on page 68.

Be True to Yourself

Gramma Tala reminded Moana that it's important to always be true to yourself.

Now it's your turn!

My name is:

....

My birthday is:

....

I was born here:

....

Draw a picture of yourself, or tape in a photo!

My best friends are:

....

....

My favourite animals are:

....

....

One of my earliest memories is:

....

....

My favourite thing to do is:

....

....

Someday I'd like to go on an adventure like this:

....

....

....

61

Island  Prints

You can make these pretty patterns just like the villagers of Motunui.

What you need:

Potatoes
Knife
Paints
Paintbrush
Paper

Always ask an adult to help you!

Step 1:
Make your stamps

Ask an adult to help you cut the potatoes in half and cut out the design. You could make sunshine, fish or a wave pattern.

Step 2:
Apply paint

Use a paintbrush to apply a coat of paint to your stamp.

TIP:
Why not stamp a pretty border to make your own special stationary!

COME TO MY PARTY!

Hello Auntie! Thank you for my present! love Molly x

Step 3:
Stamp

Press the stamp on the paper and hold it down for a few seconds. Let the paint dry.

Who said That?

Match these quotes to the characters who said them.

Gramma Tala

a

"Aboard my **boat**, I will sail across the **sea** and restore the **heart** of **Te Fiti**!"

Chief Tui

Maui

Answers on page 68.

b

"You must **learn** where you're meant to be."

c

"The ocean **choose** you, **Moana.**"

d

"I am a **demigod** and I will **smite** you!"

Moana

Colour copy

Would you like to draw loyal **Pua?** Carefully copy each square in the box above into the matching empty squares below.

Moana is Pua's **best** friend! Who is **your** best friend?

Answers

Page 13
Family and Friends
c is odd one out.

Page 14
Feathered Friends

1
2
3
4
5
6

Page 15
Where's the Water?

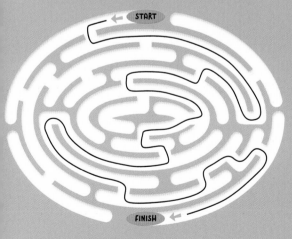

Page 18
Hidden Message
LOOK TO THE STARS
LISTEN TO THE SEA

Page 19
Wayfinder Wordsearch

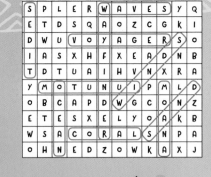

Page 24
Kakamora Confusion
There are 7 kakamora.

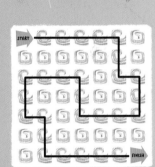

Page 25
Wayfinding

Pages 28–29
Spot the Difference

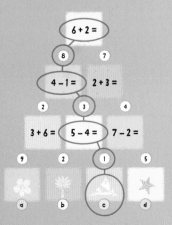

Pages 32–33
Tricky Teasers

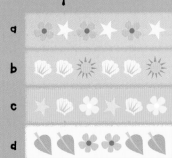

a
b
c
d

6 + 2 =
8   7
4 – 1 =   2 + 3 =
2   3   4
3 + 6 =   5 – 4 =   7 – 2 =
9   2   1   5
a   b   c   d

67

Answers

Page 39
Big Picture

Page 44
Shadow Match

a – 3, b – 2, c – 1.

Page 45
Tamatoa's Treasure

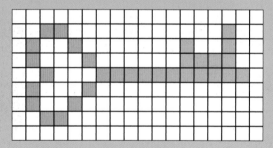

Page 46
Odd One Out

e is odd one out.

Page 47
Memory Challenge

1. Heihei   2. 1
3. false   4. true
5. true

Pages 48-49
Perfect Pairs

a & q   b & l   c & r
d & e   f & p   g & o
i & s   j & n   k & m
h doesn't have a pair.

Page 54
How Well do you know Moana?

1 - b, 2 - c, 3 - a, 4 - a, 5 - b, 6 - c,
7 - b, 8 - c.

Pages 56-57
Navigation Challenge

Page 59
A Puzzling Scene

Pieces c and e are missing.

Pages 64-65
Who Said That?

a – Moana   b – Chief Tua
c – Gramma Tala   d – Maui

Step into Anna and Elsa's magical world with Disney Frozen magazine!

From the movie

Disney FROZEN magazine!

INSIDE
❄ Puzzles
❄ Stories
❄ Colouring

FREE gift with every issue

Lights up!

© Disney

FREE Light-up Wand
WITH MAGICAL SOUNDS

From the Movie
FROZEN

From the movie
Disney FROZEN

WIN!
Disney ON ICE TICKETS!

OVER 80 STICKERS inside

2 Pretty POSTERS

cut out + make
Anna + Elsa MASKS
turn to see...

SOLVE Icy puzzles

DECORATE a poster

BATTERIES INCLUDED!

Packed with Frozen fun!

Gifts may vary

PLUS
Lots of stickers!

ON SALE every 3 weeks!

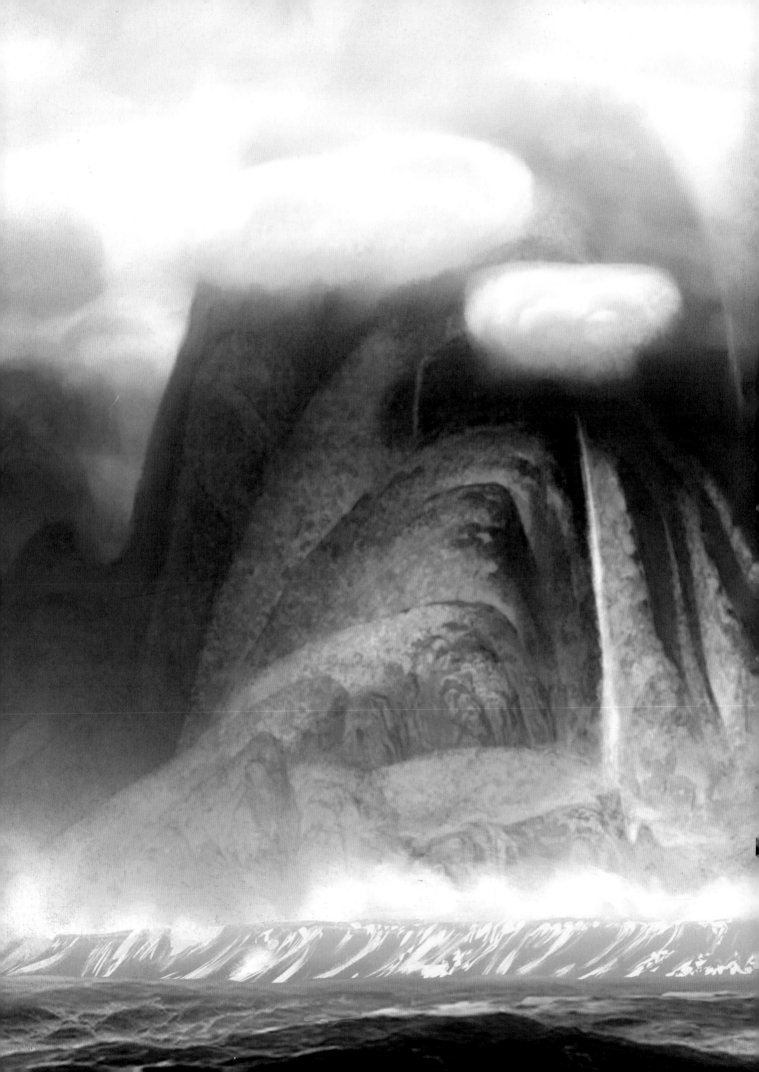